THE FIRST SNOW OF WINTER

Michaela Morgan

from the story by Graham Ralph

Illustrated by Sue Tong

BBC

Hardback edition first published in 1998 by BBC Worldwide Limited
Hardback edition reprinted in 1999
Paperback edition published in 1999 by BBC Worldwide Limited
Woodlands, 80 Wood Lane, London W12 0TT

ISBN 0 563 55513 0
ISBN 0 563 55643 9 (paperback)

Text by Michaela Morgan © BBC Worldwide Ltd, 1998
Illustrations by Sue Tong © BBC Worldwide Ltd, 1998

Based on the original animation *The First Snow of Winter*, produced by
Hibbert Ralph Entertainment and Link Entertainment for the BBC.
Licensed by Link Licensing.
From an original story by Graham Ralph.
© Link Entertainment/Hibbert Ralph Entertainment, 1998.

Printed and bound in France by Imprimerie Pollina s.a.

In the west of Ireland, there is a beautiful place
where the river meets the sea and the mists roll in with the waves.
All sorts of birds live here – corncrake and kittywake,
redshank and greenshank, golden plover and wild swans.
And ducks live here too, flocks and flocks of ducks.

One of the youngest ducks is Sean.
This is his story.

"HaHAAAAA!"

The sky was filled with gulls scattering and screeching. Sean Duck was running amuck – again. He was up to one of his favourite tricks – scaring the gulls.

"Aww, don't do that," said his best friend Puffy, the puffin. "Gulls have feelings too…"

But Sean was already looking for another adventure.

He went to the top of the steepest, slipperiest riverbank and he was off, bumping and bouncing down, faster and faster until… he landed, skimming like a stone across the water. And found himself on the other side – beak to nose with the fierce Fox! Fox was always on the prowl and juicy ducklings were one of his favourite snacks.

"Arrgh!" shouted Sean.

Sean ran. He heard the snarls of Fox close behind him, and the snap of sharp teeth drawing closer and closer. Then he felt Fox's hot breath on his neck.

"Fly, Sean, fly!" shouted Puffy. "Ducks can fly – foxes can't!"

Sean flapped desperately. Just in time, he took off to the safety of the sky.

All Fox got was a mouthful of mud and one feather.

But Sean was not out of trouble yet. He still had his mother to deal with. She had been looking for him everywhere…

"Sean Seamus Aloishus Dermot Duck!" shouted Mrs Duck. "Just what d'you think you're doing? Do you not remember what day it is?"

"Erm… Thursday?" Sean tried, hopefully.

"Oh!" Puffy remembered. "Today is the day. The big day."

"Exactly," said Ma. "Today is the day all us birds fly south for winter. So why aren't you two little featherbrains at home, getting ready?"

"Sorry, Mrs Duck," said Puffy. With a last look at his best friend, he started to trudge off home.

"Bye, Puffy," called Sean.

Ma looked down at her youngest duck. "Now don't look so down at beak. You'll see your friend again in the spring. Hurry along. We've got a long, long way to fly… if we don't want to freeze here."

As the Duck family prepared to take off, Ma gathered them around her.

"From now on," said Ma, "we must stick together. You must all listen and do as you are told – and that means *you* as well, Sean!"

Sean was only half-listening. He was too excited about following the other birds south, to their safe winter-nesting grounds.

"Is everybody ready?" asked Ma. "We are cleared for take off! 3 2 1 – go!"

At first, Sean stayed close to his family. But it wasn't very long before he spotted some gulls.

"Ha ha!" he thought. "I'll just give them a bit of a scare."

Sean zoomed down at the gulls. He swooped and dive-bombed them. The gulls scattered, screeching.

"Hooray!" Sean cheered. "See what I did, Ma! Ma…?"

There was no answer. Sean looked up and all around him but he couldn't see any of his family. The sky was almost empty.

He had been left behind.

Sean listened carefully, hoping to hear a friendly quack, but all he could hear was a deep, distant rumbling. There was a big, black shadow in the distance. It was getting closer.

"M-Ma?" he trembled. "Is that you?"

Suddenly, a huge metal monster burst through the clouds – heading straight for the terrified Sean!

"Go away, you big bald bully bird!" Sean shouted.

But the monster just roared even louder. It started to suck Sean into its spinning metal teeth.

"Help! H E L P!" yelled Sean. "Leave me alone!"

The struggle only lasted a few seconds. Then, as quickly as it had appeared from the clouds, the aeroplane was gone.

But Sean had been blown about so much that now he couldn't fly. Feathers scattering, he fell from the clouds, until he landed with a plop back in the water.

Anxiously, Sean looked up to the sky where his mum had been. No-one was there – not a duck or a puffin, not even a gull. All he could see was a big, empty sky.

Sean felt very small and very, very alone.

"MA!" he screamed "Come back! Don't leave me here!"

There was no reply. Only the sound of the wind in the reeds and a chill in the air.

The little duck flapped his wings and tried to fly. Ouch! His wing really hurt. He tried again. Ouch! Sean fell flat on his beak. His wing was broken.

"Looks to me like your flight has been cancelled!" said a cheery voice above him.

Sean looked up. He saw two strange feet, one fat and furry body and a big, smiling face.

"Voley the water vole, at your service," said the strange-looking animal. "I saw what happened up there and I can lend a paw. I have a couple of sure-fire, tried-and-tested, never-been-known-to-fail flying plans."

Voley gathered together some twigs and some leaves and strapped them onto the little duck's back.

"Are you sure this will work?" asked Sean.

"Sure – you're talking to one of Ireland's greatest pilots. Now just flap your feet and off you go…"

Sean flew and then… Crash! Sean fell.

"Ah," said Voley. "Time for plan B. All we need is a springy tree and…"

The little duck flew off into the air. He flew a bit further but then… Crash! He fell all the harder.

Voley picked his new friend up. "Hmm. It looks as if you won't be flying south for the winter after all," said the helpful vole. "Now what will become of you?"

Meanwhile, Mrs Duck had realised that Sean was missing. At once, she turned round and flew all the way back to where their journey had started. Now she was wandering through the reeds, flapping and calling out as she searched high and low for her youngest duckling.

"Sean… Sean…" she cried. "Where are you?"

And then she saw Fox. He was licking his lips – and he had feathers stuck to his snout. They looked very like Sean's feathers.

"My baby! My duckling!" sobbed Mrs Duck. "My poor little Sean – captured – and *eaten*… Oh, Sean! If only I'd kept you closer under my wing."

It was with a very heavy heart that Mrs Duck finally set off to catch up with the rest of her family.

If only Sean's mother had known that Sean was safe and close by – and that he was looking for her!

Day after day he searched, but he couldn't find her.

"Why the long beak?" Voley asked him, eventually. "With this little splint here, your arm will soon be better!"

"I miss my mother," Sean whispered.

Voley smiled gently and patted the sad little duck. "We all miss our mothers, lad, but yours will be back, come the spring. In the meantime, let's cheer you up…"

Voley sprang to his feet. "How about a hooley?" he asked, and he went high-kicking around the fields. "A hooley? You mean, a party?" Sean asked. Voley was too busy dancing to answer. So Sean put his worries aside and started dancing too.

Voley even persuaded the sheep to join in.

"Sure, I trained 'em meself," said Voley. "Come on, you hoofers! Get those toes twinkling... and SMILE!"

The sheep did their best. And Sean couldn't stop smiling.

"You're the kindest friend a duck could have," the little duck told Voley.

Just as the party ended, something soft and cold and wet landed on Sean's head.

"Ooh, that tickles!" laughed Sean. "What is it, Voley?"

"That's a snowflake, son," said Voley, anxiously. "And that means we've got to get busy. We have to find you some food and a warm shelter, to keep you going through the winter."

On the beach, Voley found an old boat. "Won't *that* make a perfect shelter!" he said. Sean wasn't so sure.

Sean was even less sure when he saw the food Voley had collected for him. Berries and nuts!

"Ducks don't *eat* nuts," said Sean, looking at the hazelnuts and acorns.

"They'd be nuts not to," said Voley. "You'll need to keep your strength up. It's going to be bitterly cold."

"Where did you get them?" Sean asked.

Voley looked a bit shifty. "The squirrels had some spare," he answered. In fact, Voley had been so rude to the poor squirrels that they had thrown nuts from their winter store at him. Then Voley had gathered the nuts up, and 'borrowed' them for Sean. But Voley decided to keep that a secret.

"That reminds me…" Voley dumped the nuts into Sean's arms before leaping onto a startled sheep.

"What are you doing now, Voley?" said Sean, in astonishment.

"You'll see!" Voley called. "Did I ever tell you about the time I was a cowbooooooy!" And he rode off into the distance.

Voley was soon back with a pile of wool. "I was just borrowing this to keep you snug as a bug," he explained, laughing.

With their work done, Sean and Voley started to walk back to Sean's shelter. It was then, through the trees, that Voley caught a glimpse of reddish fur. Fox was back.

"Quick, Sean!" said Voley. "Hide!"

Fox had seen them, too. Voley and Sean tried to hide beneath a tree trunk, but Fox soon sniffed them out. The friends had to run again, and as they raced through the forest, Fox was just behind.

Quick-thinking Voley had a plan. He stopped at a tall tree. "Oy, squirrels!" he shouted. "You're all a bunch of nutters! Rats with perms!"

"Him again!" thought the squirrels crossly, and they lobbed their hardest nuts at him. Showers of acorns, hazelnuts and conkers rained down. Voley and Sean hopped out of the way and it was Fox who got the full onslaught.

The two friends got away. "Voley," said Sean, "you're my hero."

But the next day, Voley had some awful news for Sean.

"Ahem," Voley began. Sean could tell something was wrong. "Now Sean, ducks are ducks. But voles are… different. Ducks are supposed to fly south for winter, but voles have to sleep right through. In fact it's well past my bedtime now…

…and I have to be going."

"No!" begged Sean. "*Voley* – please don't leave me here all alone."

"Sure, you'll be fine here." A sorry-looking Voley had already turned to go. "You've got your warm shelter to keep you from the cold, and wool to snuggle into, and all those nuts and berries…"

Voley was slowly moving away. "I'm sorry lad…" he said. "I have to go."

Voley was almost out of sight. Sean could just catch his last words. "Look out for the lambs. Lambs mean spring. And spring means…"

Voley was gone.

Sean huddled in his shelter and thought of all he had lost – his friend, Puffy, his mum and family, and now Voley, who had protected him. Surely such a small duck could never make it through the winter alone?

Around him the snow fell in flurries, faster and faster. The east wind blew bitterly. The old boat groaned as the wind buffeted it. Then there was a crack as the boat started to split and break into bits. Soon there was almost nothing left of Sean's shelter.

Lashed by snow, and with nowhere to go, the little duck set off, looking for any kind of place to hide. There were no nests to go to, or warm burrows. But he did find an old rubber boot. It was dry and warmly lined. So Sean climbed inside.

And that is where he spent his first winter night – alone in a storm, dreaming of friends, family and home.

The next morning, Sean peeped his beak out of the top of the boot and saw that the world had turned white. It was silent and soft, muffled under a blanket of crisp snow.

Sean wandered through this new world, admiring his own trail of webbed footprints and marvelling at the strange shapes the snow made. After a while, it almost seemed as if his eyes were playing tricks on him. There was even one humped shape that looked just like his old friend, Puffy.

Sean rubbed his eyes. It *was* Puffy!

Puffy was lying still as a stone, almost covered in snow. Sean ran up to him and hugged him. But Puffy did not move.

Sean dragged the frozen puffin back to the boot and tried to warm him up. "Wake up Puffy! Wake up, please!" he begged.

Puffy opened one tired eye. "So many birds," he muttered. "So much sea. I couldn't find my mum and dad…"

"Take it easy, Puffy," said Sean, gently. "I can look after you now."

Day after day, week after windswept week, Sean found food to feed his best friend, and wool to keep him warm.

And, from somewhere, Sean also found he had the strength to keep Puffy's spirits up.

"Keep your beak up!" he told Puffy during the long nights. "If we can just make it through these hard days, we'll have a hooley come spring. You should see me dance! I was taught by one of the best dancers in all of Ireland."

Little by little the world turned from white to grey, from brown to green.

One morning, when Sean woke up in the boot and sniffed the air, it smelt different – fresh and new. When Sean and Puffy looked out of the boot, they found a lamb looking in.

"It's spring!" yelled Sean.

The startled lamb skipped away to find his flock.

"Come back!" shouted Sean. "I'm a friend. Haven't I danced with your mother?"

"We've made it," sighed Sean. "Our parents will be back soon. Let's look for them!"
Sean's wing was still hurting him and he couldn't fly, so the little duck half-walked, half-ran towards a high, rocky clifftop. Puffy flew alongside him. At the top, the little birds eagerly scanned the skies. They looked left, then right, then left again. Then they looked behind them.

Fox was just inches away.

Sean did the only thing a duck could do. He bit Fox on the nose!

Then Sean and Puffy ran for their lives. They raced over grassland and across the beach until they spotted a boat in the harbour. The two friends scrambled across some narrow ropes and collapsed on the deck.

"We're safe," said Sean.

But he was wrong. For suddenly, with a thump, Fox landed on the deck. He had jumped after them. He was right in front of them. Behind them was a high wall. Sean and Puffy were trapped.

And then they heard a shout from above.

"Look out belooooow!"

Sean couldn't believe his eyes. Voley was swinging towards them on a rope.

"Vole Patrol to the rescue!" cried Voley.

Voley swung towards Fox and knocked him full in the face. Fox fell to the ground, stunned.

"Oh, Voley, you came back!" Sean beamed.

"Don't I always keep my word?" Voley said. "Now make yourself scarce before that Fox wakes up…"

But Fox was already standing. He snarled at Voley.

"Leave it to me, lads," said the brave vole.

Voley didn't have a chance. Fox pounced. He seized Voley in his jaws and shook him from side to side.

"VOLEY!" screamed Sean.

Fox dropped the limp body of Voley and turned around to see who had shouted.

"Hide, Puffy!" cried Sean, and he was gone – running off down the boat, back across the rope and onto the land. He ran as fast as his webbed feet would carry him.

Sean was fast. But Fox was faster.

So when Sean came to a steep slope that led down to the river, he had no choice. Although the slope was so high it made the little duck dizzy, Sean flung himself down without hesitating.

Fox followed.

Sean bumped and bounced down the slope towards the water. He flapped more and more frantically until the splint flew off his wing and…

He took off! He could fly again!

But Fox couldn't fly.

Fox couldn't swim very well either. So it was a sad and soggy Fox that finally pulled himself from the muddy weeds and trailed off home.

The victorious Sean flew back to the boat. "I did it Voley! I beat Fox," he said.

But Voley didn't reply. Voley didn't move.

Puffy was leaning over the beaten body of the faithful vole and shaking his head sadly, but Sean didn't give up. He stroked Voley's head and rubbed his paws, and all the time he talked and talked, as if he could talk the life back into him.

"You've got to wake up, Voley! I've got so much to tell you. I can fly again. I can fly!"

No movement at all.

Then a whisker twitched. An eyelid fluttered. And a weak voice said, "Sure, didn't I tell you if you flapped your feet hard enough, one day you'd make it?"

"Voley!" Sean cried, hugging his friend with all his might.

"Mind me bones! Mind me bruises!" Voley complained.

But his voice was almost drowned out by a yelp of excitement from Puffy.

"Look! Look!" he shouted, pointing to the horizon.

Just as Voley had promised, the birds were back for spring.

Soon the air was full of the sound of beating wings and bird cries. Puffy found his parents almost straight away.

"Mine must be there, too!" Sean told Voley. He flew up to the crowded sky. There they all were: corncrakes and kittywakes, redshanks and greenshanks, golden plover and wild swans – and flocks and flocks of ducks. Sean darted in and out between them.

"Is that you, Ma? Oh, sorry. Excuse me… has anyone seen my parents? Wait! Hang on… has anyone seen my mother?"

Gradually the sky cleared. All the birds had passed by.

Sean flew back to the boat, where Voley was waiting.

"They didn't come back for me after all," he whispered.

Then, from behind a high and hazy cloud, he heard a very familiar voice.

"Why are we always the last to go and the last to return?" grumbled Mrs Duck at her family, as they straggled along at the back.

"Ma! Da! It's me!" yelled Sean.

"SEAN! I thought the fox had got you!" his mother cried, as the Duck family swooped joyfully down to the boat deck.

"Who, that old fox?" said Sean. "I sent him for a ducking! Oh Ma, the things I've done! The things I've learnt! Don't you think I'm grown up now?"

His mother smiled. "Not too grown up to come under your mother's wing, I hope," she said. Then she opened her big, soft wings and wrapped them around her dear little duckling.

Sean sighed happily. "Home at last," he said.

THE END

Speaking and Listening

Yackety-yak, the Alien's Back

Pie Corbett
and Ruth Thomson

Chrysalis Children's Books

First published in the UK in 2004 by
Chrysalis Children's Books
An imprint of Chrysalis Books Group Plc
The Chrysalis Building,
Bramley Road,
London, W10 6SP

Paperback edition first published in 2005

ISBN 1 84138 965 X (hb)
ISBN 1 84458 311 2 (pb)

British Library Cataloguing in Publication Data
for this book is available from the British Library.

Editorial manager: Joyce Bentley
Editor: Nicola Edwards
Designers: Rachel Hamdi, Holly Mann
Illustrators: Jan McCafferty, Guy Parker-Rees,
Liz Pichon and Gwyneth Williamson

Printed in China

Contents

3

Speaking and listening

Talking helps children to think, communicate and make sense of the world around them. Children's speech flourishes where there are interesting activities to talk about. This happens through play, discussing what is happening around them, looking at interesting objects and books and talking about events at home or in school.

Recounting what the family or class has done and inventing stories together

Yackety-yak, I'm big and I'm back!

are helpful ways to develop talk and the imagination. Saying funny sentences, inventing rhymes and singing are also important.

About this book

This book is designed for adults (whether parents, carers or teachers) and children to talk about together. It is brimming with activities that will give children opportunities to talk out loud, to develop their abilities to speak in a wide variety of ways and to listen carefully.

The activities

Each double page has a particular focus (see the contents page) and is completely self-contained. You can open the book at any page, talk together about what you see in the detailed pictures and go backwards or forwards at whim.

However, although the book has no fixed order, the activities in the first half are generally easier than those in the second half. The early pages encourage children to play with words, use alliteration, create riddles and describe and compare, using complex sentences. Later pages stimulate children to respond at greater length, complaining, advising, making up stories and problem solving.

You do not need to do all the activities on each page at one sitting – the book has been deliberately

designed to be re-read again and again, with more things to discover at each re-reading.

Extension activities

There are further suggestions of things to do related to each theme on pages 30 and 31. These, in turn, may prompt you to invent more activities of your own.

Talking and listening guidelines

There are suggested guidelines for how good speakers and listeners behave on page 32.

How to use this book

The four activities at the bottom of each double page provide starting points for conversation. Some invite children to discuss what they see and to use talk in an exploratory way. Others require a more formal response, using particular sentence structures and vocabulary. In some cases, sentence openers or models are given. These are merely suggestions for developing different types of sentence or vocabulary, such as comparatives or the use of time connectives (eg then, after), which will help children develop their talk beyond one or two word comments. You could also lead from a talking session into writing.

The pictures have been drawn so that there are usually many different possible responses – since an atmosphere of 'getting it right or wrong' will not encourage children to speak up. Children talk best when they feel relaxed and the people around them

are interested in what they have to say. If children seem uncertain, begin by modelling a sentence structure (the text preceded by the speech bubble). Try to avoid firing questions that require one word answers. Use phrases such as 'tell me…', which invite more extended replies.

Talk partners

You may find it helpful to ask the children to 'think, share in a pair', before giving a response in front of a whole class. Working with a talk partner provides a chance to think together and sort out what might be said. It is also helpful if you can model a few possible responses, so that the children might listen and think carefully for themselves, before they rehearse their own reply in pairs and say it aloud in front of the class.

The focus of the talking activity

The talking activity that you ask the child to do.

A sample answer you might expect from the child.

The sentence structure you could encourage the child to use.

A wonderful world of wildlife
Use sounds and rhymes.

★ **I spy**

Play 'I spy' using sounds or letters, eg '**t**'.
Try using beginning, end or middle sounds.

○ **I spy** two things **that end with 't**.

○ Goa**t** and new**t** both end with '**t**'.

★ **Rhyme it**

In the picture, find things that rhyme with **bar**, **toy**, **how**, **stair** and **poor**. Then choose a creature, eg **fox**, and think of a word that rhymes with it.

○ Box **rhymes with** fox.

★ **Alphabet challenge**

Look for animals for each letter of the alphabet. How many creatures can you find that start with the same letter?

○ **K**angaroo and **k**oala both start with 'k'.

★ **Riddles**

Choose an animal, eg an owl, and make up three clues about it. Who can guess your riddle?

○ **I am thinking of an animal that** starts with 'o', rhymes with 'trowel' and flies at night.

What is it like? Play with words.

⭐ **Invent riddles**

Choose an object, eg the spade, and make up three clues about it. Who can guess your riddle?

💬 I am made of metal. I work by digging deep. Birds sit on me when I rest.

⭐ **Crazy sentences**

Choose an object. Pretend that it comes alive. Make up a crazy sentence about it.

💬 The sack sat in the corner twiddling its thumbs.

✦ **Invent tongue twisters**

Choose an object and invent a tongue twister about it.

◯ The **s**ilver, **s**lippery **s**aw **s**ailed **s**ilently as the **s**lithery **s**nake **s**neaked by **s**lyly.

✦ **Create funny similes**

Choose an object and invent a simile about it.

◯ **The broom is like** a giraffe's neck.

The broom is like a stick of rock.

The broom is like a busy teacher!

Alien spotting
Find similarities and differences.

★ **Which one?**

Take it in turns to describe an alien
for someone else to find.

◯ This alien has...

★ **Spot the similarities**

Choose two aliens that share two similarities
for someone else to find.

◯ These two aliens both have...

★ **Spot the difference**

Choose two or three aliens.

Explain how they are different.

🗨 These aliens are different **because** one has...
and the other one has...

★ **Similarities and differences**

Point to two aliens. Explain how they are
similar and how they are different.

🗨 These aliens **both have**... **and**... **but**...

Who lives where?
Use descriptive language.

✦ Matching game

Describe a character and the house they live in. Who can match the character to the house?

💬 Which lady in red with the flowery hat, lives at the house with the green door?

✦ Tell me where

Choose a house or character and give three clues about where it is. Use words like, 'below, above, beside, behind, near, next to and in between'. Who can guess the house or character you have chosen?

💬 Which house is **between**...?

✦ Ask questions

Take turns to ask a question about a person or house for someone else to answer.

💬 Which is the house with a cat on the roof?

✦ Spot the difference

Choose a pair of houses or characters and explain the differences between them.

💬 **The differences between... and... are that...**

What's all the fuss?

Describe what you can see.

★ **What can you see?**

List three things that you can see on the pirate ship, using only one sentence.

💬 **On the pirate ship I can see** a boy mopping the deck, a cook carrying a fish **and** a dog fast asleep.

★ **Watch out!**

Choose a pirate in the first picture and warn him or her about what is about to happen.

💬 **Watch out because** the hammock is about to collapse!

14

✴ **How are they feeling?**

Choose someone in the second picture.

Explain how they are feeling, and why.

◯ The pirate in the crow's nest is cross **because** a seagull has flown off with her hat.

✴ **What next?**

Choose something that is happening in the second picture and say what might happen next.

◯ The sharks might eat the pirate who has been pulled overboard.

Find the way
Give directions.

✦ Find the stall
Choose a stall and give three clues about where it is. Use words like, 'below, above, beside, behind, near, next to and in between'. Who can guess the stall you have chosen?

💬 Which stall **has a**... and is in **front of**... and **next to**...?

✦ Which way?
Choose two stalls and describe how you would get from one stall to the other.

💬 **To get from** the stall selling fish **to** the stall selling eggs **I would**...

✦ This way!
Choose a character and give them instructions about how to get to a stall. Use words like, 'turn left, turn right, go along, keep going straight on'.

💬 Mrs Singh, **to get to the** book stall...

✦ Time for tea
Give each character instructions for how to get to the tea stall.

💬 Mr Williams, **to get to the tea stall**...

Mike Smith

Zoe Lee

Mr Williams

Paula Cortez

Mrs Young

Dr Chang

Mrs Singh

Adam Stone

17

Whatever next? Tell the tale.

★ **What's happening?**

Choose a set of pictures and tell the story of what is happening.

◯ The princess was locked in the tower. A prince came to rescue her. But he hadn't noticed the dragon...

★ **What happened before?**

Invent a sentence to explain what has happened before the set of pictures, starting with the word 'before'.

◯ **Before** she was captured by the dragon, the princess...

★ **Talk to them**

Imagine you could talk to the different characters.
What would you say to each other?

◯ Watch out! There's a dragon behind you!

◯ Thanks! What's it doing?

★ **What happens next?**

Invent a sentence to explain what happens next,
using the word 'after'.

◯ **After** the prince saw the dragon, there
was a fierce fight.

Sort it out!
Complain and give advice.

★ **What's up?**

Choose a problem and explain what has gone wrong.
◯ The hot air balloon has a puncture and all the gas is coming out. The passengers in the basket are looking worried.

★ **Complain**

Work in pairs. Imagine one of you has taken the faulty goods back. Complain to the shopkeeper.
◯ This hot air balloon has got a puncture. You should give me a new one!

★ **Silly solutions**

Suggest silly ways to solve the problem.

💬 **Can I suggest that you** use some chewing gum to mend the puncture and then the balloon will fly beautifully.

★ **What next?**

Choose something that is going wrong in the picture. Tell the story of what happens next.

💬 The balloon began to fall to the ground. Luckily, it landed on a bouncy castle and everyone was saved.

Danger island
Describe the dangers and give advice.

★ **What will happen?**

There is trouble ahead on Danger island!
Take it in turns to suggest what might happen.

💬 If the man steps on the snake, **then** the snake might bite him!

★ **What would they say?**

Say what you think each person might shout out.

💬 Help – the tree is shaking!

Oh no! That bear looks hungry!

★ **Impossible advice**

Tell the people how to avoid disaster. Invent impossible ideas for how they could escape.

💬 **To avoid** being eaten by the crocodile, simply sprout wings and fly away.

★ **You'll never guess...**

Pretend you are one of the people on the island and tell a friend what happened to you.

💬 It was so hot that I wanted to cool off. So, I jumped into the water. Suddenly, a shark appeared...

The story café
Pick ingredients for a story.

✦ Choose a goodie

Pick a 'goodie' as your main character. (You could use dice to help you choose.) Think about where your character might live. Invent three things about your character.

💬 **There was once** a cat called Frankie, who lived in a forest. She had sleek, ginger fur and she loved eating mangoes.

✦ Choose a magical object

Pick a magical object for your character to find. What magical powers does the object have?

💬 The magic cloak makes anyone who puts it on able to fly.

✦ Pick a baddie

Choose a bad character to appear in your story. What is he or she like? Where does he or she live? Invent three things about your character.

💬 The snake lives in a cave. It can destroy things by breathing on them. It never tells the truth.

✦ Making links

Practise making links between your goodie, your baddie and the magical object. Use the story connectives on the menu board in the story café.

💬 **Suddenly** the snake appeared. **As** it slithered towards her, Frankie wrapped herself in the magic cloak.

• Now turn the page and use your characters to tell a story about a journey.

MENU

Once upon a time	Suddenly
Early one morning	So
One day	Next
At that moment	Then
When	Eventually
As	After that
As soon as	Finally
Immediately	In the end
Before	
After	
Once	
Whenever	
While	
During	

The story island

Mix ingredients for a story.

★ **Pick a setting**

Choose a place on the island where your character will begin his or her journey. What is the place like? Why is your character there?

◯ Frankie lived in the forest, underneath her favourite mango tree. The forest was dark and silent.

★ **Choose a destination**

Pick a place where your character's journey will end. Why is the journey necessary?

◯ Frankie has to travel to the cave in the mountains to fetch some medicine for the old king who is ill.

★ **What happens?**

What goes wrong on the journey? What part does the magical object play? Use the map to think of some ideas. Which baddies does your character meet on the way?

◯ Frankie finds a crystal ball that shows her how to escape from traps. Then she meets a cat-eating troll.

★ **The end**

How does your character get round all the problems? Tell the story, using connectives and adverbs. How does your story end?

Story adverbs

angrily
bravely
carefully
cautiously
desperately
foolishly
quickly
quietly
silently
slowly

27

Can you fix it? Solve the problems.

★ **Watch out!**

Find a problem in the picture.

🗨 The cat is trying to reach the baby birds.
It might attack them.

★ **Solve it**

Discuss different ideas for solving the problem.

🗨 You could... You might... If you...
How about... Supposing...

28

★ **Will it work?**

Listen to some ideas and discuss their strengths and weaknesses.

💬 I like the idea… **because**… **but** you might find that…

★ **Crazy ideas**

Try inventing some really crazy solutions.

💬 The cat could put on a snorkel and swim across to fetch the toy from the pond!

Extension activities

The pictures in this book are designed to generate talk for all sorts of purposes. When children are talking, encourage them to speak up sufficiently loudly and clearly so that everyone can hear and you do not have to repeat what they have said. Mirror standard versions back to them or ask them to complete what has been said, especially if it is fragmentary or over relies on gesture.

Give praise to those who have listened well and responded with questions or answers. In group or paired work, taking turns is a crucial step forward which needs to be modelled by the teacher and praised. At this age, group work needs careful structuring so that everyone knows their role in the group. This will need practice and discussion.

When a presentation is being given, encourage children to identify key points in what is being said. Focus their listening by asking them to locate specific points and recall them afterwards.

Constant inventing, telling and retelling of stories, using traditional language will help children to internalise basic patterns of narrative, including sentence patterns.

Use simple role-play and improvisation to act out scenes based on children's own experiences. This can easily arise out of the pictures in this book by asking children to select characters or an event and act it out or discuss what happened retrospectively.

Pages 6-7   A wonderful world of wildlife
This double spread provides practice in the ability to identify sounds in words and rhyming patterns. It encourages children to think about letters of the alphabet and create simple riddles. You could also use the spread to focus on sounds in different ways.
✦ Practise simple segmentation by asking children to find animals that have 3 (rat), 4 (tiger) or 5 (koala) sounds.
✦ Choose a creature and see who can list the largest number of rhymes, eg rat – sat, bat, cat, mat, flat and so on.
✦ Ask the children to role-play the discussion going on in the car!

Pages 8-9   What is it like?
These two pages provide practice in inventing simple riddles, simple personification, alliteration and similes. It is not important for children to know the names of the effects that they are using and the key to the spread is that it should be playful and enjoyable. Give children time to work in pairs inventing their sentences so that they have time to 'think' and discuss with their partner before they come together to 'share' their ideas.
✦ Ask questions based on the five senses, such as: 'Can you find me something that is smooth to touch and good to look at?' (eg book).
✦ Use the spread to play *I-spy*, finding rhymes for different items.
✦ Ask the children to describe items and see who can guess what they are describing.

Pages 10-11   Alien spotting
This double spread is packed with aliens! It can be used to practise simple description and discrimination, thinking about similarities and differences.
✦ Ask the children to name different aliens and consider what they might be able to do. Talk about where they could hide in a house and discuss whether they have superpowers.
✦ Ask the children to imagine what might happen if an alien lived in their classroom.
✦ The children could create their own aliens and add them to the discussion.

Pages 12-13   Who lives where?
This double spread provides further practice in using precise descriptive language, using positional language such as 'above', 'beside', or 'below' as well as asking questions and spotting differences.
✦ Ask the children to give names to the characters and describe them – what they are wearing, how they behave and how they speak. Discuss what they might be like, considering which characters might be goodies and which could be baddies in a story. Discuss what sort of story the characters might be in.
✦ Choose a character and act out a simple situation, such as buying a bar of chocolate.
✦ Use the picture as a starting point for making up stories. Choose only a few of the characters each time and invent conversations between them.

Pages 14-15   What's all the fuss?
This double page provides opportunities to use language in different ways – to describe, to warn and to recount in the past and future tense.
✦ Choose a pirate and discuss what he or she might say in each picture.
✦ Put different pirates 'in the hot-seat' and ask the children to interview them about what has happened.
✦ Invent a television news bulletin about the pirate ship disaster.
✦ Work in pairs and hold a discussion about what has happened.

Pages 16-17   Find the way
These pages focus on using instructional language to give directions.
✦ Use the double spread to develop the children's descriptive skills – ask them to describe characters or stalls.
✦ Ask the children to choose a character and in role pretend to approach a stall and buy something or return an item and complain about its quality.
✦ In role as stall holders, ask children to try to persuade a customer to buy an item. Encourage them to use positive language to persuade their customers to buy the product.

Pages 18-19 Whatever next?

The groups of pictures provide opportunities for children to recount what has happened, is happening and what might happen next.

★ Use the pictures as a basis for storytelling. Provide story connectives that could be used, eg Once upon a time, one day, early one morning, so, next, when, while, after that, suddenly, without warning, at that moment, finally, in the end, eventually…

★ To encourage a simple pattern, ask the children to include:

- an opening
- a build up – in which the story begins
- a dilemma – where something goes wrong
- a resolution – which sorts out the problem
- an ending

★ Continue the story boards by adding more pictures – before and after the three pictures shown. Use these as a simple way to aid plotting.

Pages 20-21 Sort it out!

This double page sets up a host of different events which lend themselves to complaining and advising as well as imagining what might happen next. The idea of consequences lies at the root of storytelling.

★ Work on simple monologues that have a chosen character talking aloud, describing the various incidents.

★ Encourage the children to focus on each incident, explaining what is happening and suggesting how it might be resolved.

★ In role as journalists, the children could interview characters to discover what happened.

Pages 22-23 Danger island

This double spread encourages children to describe events, using simple recounts. It is built around a series of possible dangers that need to be avoided. It could lend itself to all sorts of possibilities for talk:

★ Ask the children to give a recount in role as a character telling a friend what happened.

★ In role as television news reporters, children could interview characters about events on the island.

★ Use the picture as a basis for simple story making.

★ Ask the children to retell events in a diary format.

Pages 24-25 The story café

The pictures on this double page can be used as an imaginative way into story making. The café provides basic ingredients to select from: various characters – goodies and baddies – settings and magical objects.

★ Let the children select one goodie, who will meet one baddie. Ask them to describe the characters and role-play with them in different situations, eg sitting on a bus together. Encourage the children to say descriptive sentences that use detail to make the characters sound real. Try sentences with three things, eg the dragon had green scales, red eyes and fire belching from its mouth.

★ Ask the children to think about where the story will start and where the action will take place, encouraging them to invent descriptions for different settings.

★ What magic object might be involved? Ask the children to describe it and decide on its special powers.

★ Use question words to begin to flesh out a story idea:

- who are the characters?
- where are they?
- what goes wrong? (the dilemma)
- when is the story set? (past or present tense)
- how will it end?

★ With the children, scan books to add to the collection of story connectives. Practise sentences using these – and if children struggle, invent some together, initially modelling several examples.

Pages 26-27 The story island

The picture map provides a chance for children to use it to invent their own story, with a simple structure.

★ Who is the main character? Where are they going? Why are they going? (Provide a simple task.) What route will they take? What awful event will befall them en route? (Bring the baddie into play!) Where do they find the magic object and how will it help them escape the main dilemma?

★ Think about a safe ending.

★ It is important to use the story connectives to help link the tale together.

★ Work out a story together as a class, then let children work in pairs to draw their own map, based on the spread and draw onto it their characters, and the main events. This can then be used as a basic plan to aid storytelling.

Pages 28-29 Can you fix it?

This double spread provides a good basis for pairs or groups to practise problem-solving. Groups should divide up simple tasks, ensuring that:

★ they keep to a time limit;
★ they keep on task;
★ one person acts as scribe and notes ideas;
★ one person is in charge;
★ everyone has a fair turn at saying what they think.

Logical solutions are welcome – but wacky ideas are also fun. Remember – the aim is for the children to share ideas and explain their reasons. It is about encouraging talking and listening – not about being 'right'.

How to be a good speaker and listener

When I speak, I need to:

★ Be ready to ask people to explain ideas further.

★ Respect ideas that I don't agree with.

★ Add more points to a discussion.

★ Give reasons for my ideas: I think. . . because. . .

★ Try to keep to the point.

★ Use expression to make what I say sound interesting.

★ Remember who I am talking with and how they might feel.

★ Suggest ideas: What if. . .?

★ Be ready to change my mind if I hear a good idea.

★ Think of things that might be interesting or useful to say or add.

★ Organise what I'm going to say with an introduction, the content and a conclusion.

★ Include relevant details.

★ Speak clearly, look at my audience and take turns.

When I listen, I need to:

★ Remember instructions and specific points.

★ Show by my expression that I am interested in the speaker.

★ Write down information or ideas that I might forget.

★ Wait my turn before speaking.

★ Look at the speaker, keep still and follow what is being said.

★ Ask about anything I don't understand.

★ Give a reply if someone asks a question.